FROM BONES TO BODIES

A Story of Paleontology

WILLIAM FOX and
SAMUEL WELLES

Drawings by
Howard E. Hamman, Jr.

New York   HENRY Z. WALCK, INC.   *1959*

ACKNOWLEDGEMENTS

GRATEFUL ACKNOWLEDGE-
MENT is made to the following sources for permission to reprint the photographs and paintings included in this book:

American Museum of Natural History: pp. 31, 92, 93, 94, 98

British Museum (Natural History): pp. 79, 87

Chicago Natural History Museum: pp. 42, 56, 66, 67, 90, 103

New York Zoological Society: p. 51

University of California: p. 77

William Fox
Samuel Welles

CONTENTS

THE PALEO-DETECTIVE AT WORK

CASE HISTORIES

THE PALEO-DETECTIVE
AT WORK

A RAT IS LIKE AN ELEPHANT

BURIED IN THE EARTH is evidence of life as it was many millions of years ago. It is the job of the paleontologist—a man who studies fossils—to examine the evidence as it is uncovered, interpret it and write the story.

The complete story of the science of paleontology would fill many books. In fact, it fills a large number now, and the story is far from finished. Parts of it will never be written, because the facts are buried too deep to be found. This book will tell only one small part of the story. It will not include fossil plants, shells or fishes, but will deal almost entirely with animals that lived on the land or in the air. It will show some of the examples of fossil evidence a scientist may have at hand and what he does with them. It will follow his thoughts as he makes up his mind about the meaning of each new fossil fact. It will tell how he can reconstruct animals from fossil evidence—how the paleontologist reasons his way from bones to bodies.

Some animals have backbones and some don't. Those that do are called vertebrates. So far as their skeletons are concerned, all vertebrate animals have much in common. In fact, they are more alike than different. This broad statement holds true even though the vertebrate group includes elephants, anteaters, rats, fishes, lizards, men and hogs.

Everyone knows that a rat and an elephant are different. But not everyone knows that they are very much alike. Both eat and drink and breathe and behave alike in a thousand ways. For the moment, forget that one is a pest and the other a circus star and think only about their skeletons.

What is the main difference? Size, of course. Certainly that is important, but it is only one difference. By using our imaginations we can make the rat and the elephant the same size. Pretend they are both about the size of a small dog and compare them on that basis.

When we see the two skeletons side by side and the same size, they look as if they were built on the same general plan. Along the top is the backbone with a skull at one end and a tail at the other. Actually, the tail is just the last section of the backbone. A "basket" made up of ribs hangs

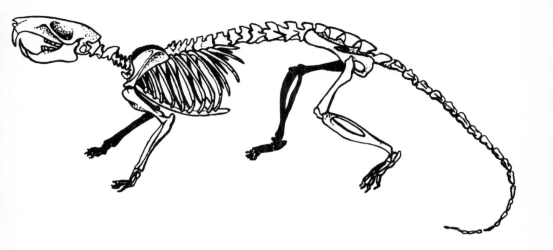

Bone for bone, the skeletons of the rat (above) and
the elephant (below) are much alike.

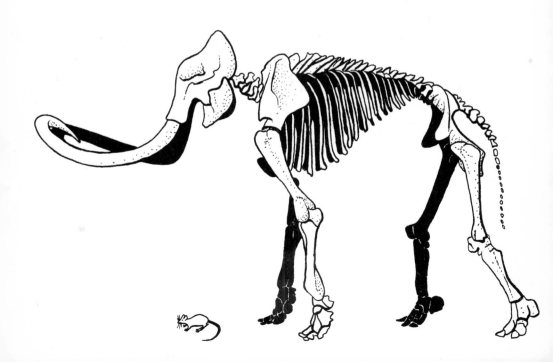

from the backbone in about the same position in both skeletons. At the front of the rib basket is the framework for the front limbs. Some distance behind the last rib is the framework for the hind limbs.

That's the plan. Rat or elephant, it is the same. Look at some of the details.

First, look closely at the skulls. The teeth appear different at first but really are rather similar. Rats have very large upper front teeth, or incisors. The fact that these are handy for gnawing holes from the attic to the kitchen is an accident. Rat teeth took shape long before there were any houses. They were used for cutting off the tough stalks of plants and for other everyday uses. In the elephant a pair of upper front teeth is enlarged, too, but in a different shape. These tusks point forward and serve as bayonets or digging tools, as the occasion demands. Farther back in the mouth both animals have grinding teeth. Yes, the teeth are more alike than different, after all.

If you could examine the skulls closely you would find in them a number of very crooked lines or cracks. These are sutures. They show where the skull bones are joined. In the skulls of baby vertebrates the bones are separate and are still soft. As the baby grows older the bones get larger and harder and press together until only this crooked line shows that they were once separate. They are joined so firmly that you would break the bones before you could

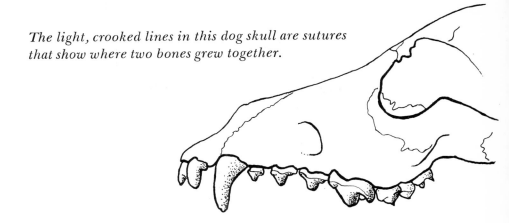

ever separate them. In the rat and elephant even the pattern formed by the sutures is about the same. There are the same number of bones in about the same positions. Another similiar skull feature is a pair of smooth knobs that fit against the backbone. Both skulls have a honeycomb type of bone inside the nose opening. The lower jaws of both are attached or hinged to the skull in about the same way.

Behind the skull, each animal has seven neck bones. These are the cervical vertebrae. Then comes a series of several bones called thoracic vertebrae, which have bumps where the ribs join them. Several pieces behind these are smooth and ribless. They are called the lumbar vertebrae. They are followed by the sacrum, a bone made up of several vertebrae "welded" together as a solid base for the hipbone or pelvis. Last comes the tail. All of these bones of the back lie end to end, like a pipeline. In a sense, they are a pipeline that protects the great spinal nerve cord which runs through an arch on the upper side of each vertebra.

Compare the rib baskets and you will find no difference of importance.

The legs and feet of these creatures at first glance seem quite different. The more we study them, however, the more alike they appear. Starting with the front leg, there is the flat scapula, or shoulder blade. It is joined rather loosely to the ribs and vertebrae. The upper armbone, or humerus, is below it. Then come the forearm bones, which are called the radius and ulna. Several small carpal and metacarpal bones make up the wrist and palm. There are five "fingers," with two joints on the first and three joints on each of the others. The finger bones are called phalanges from a Greek word meaning "battle lines."

The arrangement of the hind limbs is not much different. Unlike the shoulder bone, the hipbone is attached very firmly to the backbone. The hipbone and sacrum have grown so tightly together that they would be hard to separate. A large knob on the thighbone, or femur, fits into a hollow in the hipbone, making a ball-and-socket joint. With this kind of attachment the leg can be moved through almost a half circle. At the lower end of the thighbone, a small, loose bone protects the joint with the lower leg or shank bones. We call this the kneecap, but it is more properly known as the patella, which is Latin for a small pan or dish. The two shank bones are the tibia and fibula. The tibia is also known as the shinbone. Several ankle and palm bones and five toes complete the hind limb. The ankle and palm bones are the tarsals and metatarsals. The toes, like the fingers, are made up of phalanges.

All of these details apply to the rat skeleton and fit the elephant just as well. All in all, then, a rat and an elephant are more alike than different when their skeletons are compared as if they were the same size.

FIRST, LOOK AT THE TEETH

ONCE IN A WHILE a complete fossil skeleton is found with all of the bones in place. Then the job of the paleontologist is simple. More often some of the bones are missing, and the rest are mashed and broken. When this is the case, the rock material surrounding the bones must be chipped away and the pieces of each bone put back together like a three-dimensional jigsaw puzzle. This must be done before the scientist has a starting point.

After all of the parts are cleaned and put back together again, they can be arranged in the general shape of a skeleton. Whether this animal is a horse, a dinosaur or a squirrel, the plan will be about the same, just as in the rat and the elephant. The head will be at one end, the tail at the other, and the rest arranged in between. If only a few bones are missing, the paleontologist can usually fill in the gaps. He uses the bones he has as a pattern for the missing pieces. Where more bones are missing, the paleontologist is in the position of a detective with only a few clues. He has to reconstruct the situation by deduction. In fact, he is a detective, but, instead of crime, his problem is to add to human knowledge. He is helping to piece together the story of life—the story of how the animals we see today developed from the primitive forms of millions of years ago.

This paleo-detective has most of the evidence before him in the shape of a skeleton. From it he wants to know what this animal looked like and how it acted. Then he can better understand how it was related to other animals that lived earlier or later.

The rest of the evidence is in the rock formation where the bones were found. This may be fossil leaves, tree trunks or shells from other animals. The plant remains, particularly, tell about the climate and the surroundings in which the animal lived and died. So may the rock itself. Some rock is hardened dune sand, and must have been in a desert or on a beach. Careful study of the sand grains will show whether the rocks were desert dunes or beach sand. Footprints in certain kinds of layered rocks may show that the animal was in the habit of walking on mud flats. Probably more vertebrate fossils are found in river-delta rocks than anywhere else. Such rocks tell little about the animal's habits except that it fell in the river one time too many.

The first thing the scientist wants to see is the animal's

teeth. When he has studied them he knows what kind of food it ate, or at least whether it was a meat eater or a vegetarian.

If the animal was a meat eater, or carnivore, it will have incisor teeth for nipping, canine teeth for stabbing, scissorlike carnassials and crushers, or molars. Watch a dog as it is eating a bone with a little meat left on it. First it will use its small, sharp front teeth to nip off little pieces of tender meat. The next teeth are the long fangs, or stabbers. It won't use them except perhaps for scrapers. They are its weapons for hunting or defending itself. It pierces and

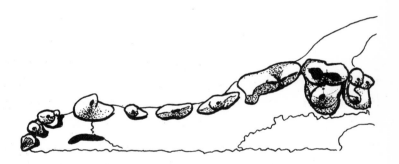

Half view of the roof of a dog's mouth, showing the different kinds of teeth.

tears with these. Behind them, around at the sides of its mouth, are the scissors, or cutting teeth. When the bone scraping gets tough, the dog turns its head and puts these to work. It will use them, too, for cutting tough meat and gristle. After the meat is all scraped off and eaten, the dog will settle down to tear the bone apart. For this heavy duty it will scrape and chisel with its scissor teeth and mash the pieces with its crushers. It will turn its head to every angle to bring the crushers to bear on a corner of bone. It tears the hard shell of bone away, bit by bit, so it can get at the marrow. That is what it was after in the first place. Dogs need bone and marrow just as we need minerals and vitamins; but dogs have to work to get them.

The teeth for the heaviest work are at the back of the mouth, closest to the jaw hinge. This gives the greatest leverage, in the same way that putting a nut in a nutcracker nearest to the hinge does.

A dog does not chew a chunk of meat over and over, as a cow does a cud of grass. Meat-eating animals do not do much chewing. Meat is easily digested and does not need to be ground to a pulp before it is swallowed. For that reason, a dog does not need a mouthful of grinders.

Some meat-eating animals became specialists, and their teeth show it. An example is the saber-toothed cat. Its fangs were much larger than those of most carnivores. Imagine a tiger with stabbing teeth ten inches long, and you have a pretty good picture of the saber-toothed cat. It had a special hinge arrangement so the lower jaw could drop

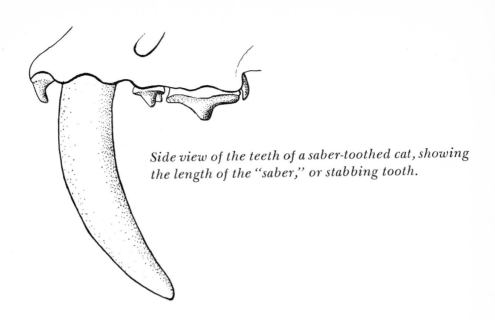

Side view of the teeth of a saber-toothed cat, showing the length of the "saber," or stabbing tooth.

down against its throat. When it hunted, this cat probably opened its mouth in the shape of a big yawn and then stabbed its prey with the sabers. While the big teeth were excellent weapons, they must have been in the way when there was shearing to be done. Perhaps the animal's main food was blood. Anyway, life must have been difficult for it, because the saber-toothed cat has been extinct for many centuries.

Suppose the scientist has found that the skeleton includes a set of meat-eater teeth. This does not mean it belongs to a dog or a cat. Those animals have merely been used as examples of meat eaters. All he knows for sure is that this animal fed itself largely on meat. But from this first bit of evidence certain things can be reasoned. If the animal ate meat it must have obtained it in one of two ways. Either it hunted its prey, or it ate what it found. Only a few animals, such as the hyena, eat leftovers. So the scientist stores this thought away as a possibility to check later and says, "This animal probably hunted." In nature, a successful hunter must be fast or clever or both. Even if it drops on its prey from the trees, as do some members of the cat family, it must be active. Many meat eaters must overtake each meal in a foot race and kill it before they eat. The chances are, then, that this meat eater was the athletic type. It had a good chest and a thin waist. It must have had sport-car styling, like a tiger, instead of truck lines, like a hippopotamus. It probably was bright-eyed and alert, because otherwise it would have become food for some animal that was.

This much the paleo-detective deduces from the teeth alone. While he is beginning to form a mental picture of the animal, he knows it may be the wrong one. As his study goes on, he will be "checking out" new bits of evidence. As each bit appears, he will check all of his ideas against it. If they hold up in the new light, fine. If they do not, he will change his mental picture until it fits all the evidence he has found.

Suppose it turns out that the teeth are not meat-eater

teeth at all. It is not hard to find out if they belong to an animal that fed on grass or leaves. In herbivores, or plant eaters, the back teeth will be flat grinders. Each of these will have low, hard ridges with small hollows in between. When such an animal chews, the motion is about as much side to side as up and down. The grinding surfaces rub past one another and wear the food down to a pulp. Unless the food is very tender, a great deal of chewing is needed. Grasses and leaves are not as easily digested as meat. They must be ground before they go to the stomach. That is why the grinder teeth are always found in animals that live almost entirely on plants. In some cases, the grinders keep growing as long as the animal lives. This is because dust, grit and other hard materials in the food wear the teeth down. If the teeth did not grow to make up for such wear, the animal would lose its grinding power before it reached middle age. Unable to grind its food, it would die.

Other than the grinders, the teeth of the vegetarians do not follow a strict pattern. The horse, for example, has nippers at the front of its mouth and small canines next. These can hardly be called stabbers, because they are so small they have lost that use. In fact, some horses have no

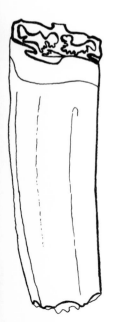

Top and side views of a horse's lower grinder tooth, showing ridges and hollows on the grinding surface.

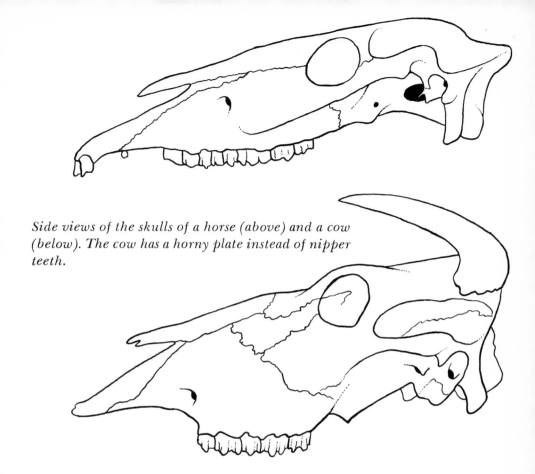

Side views of the skulls of a horse (above) and a cow (below). The cow has a horny plate instead of nipper teeth.

canines at all. Between the canines and the grinders there is a space without teeth. This is the place where the bit fits when you put the bridle on. The horse's face is so long that its eyes are above the level of the grass as it eats. Thus it is able to watch out for danger as it grazes. With a short face it would have to eat a bit and watch a bit. Being able to eat and watch at the same time, the long-faced wild horse had a longer life.

Cows do not have as many front teeth as do horses. The upper front teeth are missing entirely. Instead, there is a horny plate. The few lower front teeth that are left lie almost flat, pointing forward. To crop grass, the cow clamps a few blades between the little front teeth and the horny plate and jerks its head upward so the teeth do the cutting. Then the cow's big tongue moves the food back to the grinding department.

Some plant eaters had very special teeth. An odd-looking one was the imperial elephant. He looked much like a circus elephant except for his tusks. They were so long they curved up and crossed over each other in front. It is hard to understand how they could have been useful except as clubs or bumpers. Perhaps that is the reason the imperial elephant is no longer with us except as a fossil.

A few kinds of extinct animals apparently were not able to do enough chewing, even with grinders. They had gizzards, too. A gizzard is found mainly inside birds. It is a collection of pebbles or stones enclosed in a thick bag made of muscle. The muscles ripple around the stones and cause them to grind the food. Each time that a certain kind of dinosaur skeleton has been found, a little cluster of rounded stones has been found with it. The stones are always in the same part of the body, about where a gizzard should be. This is sound evidence that the dinosaur had a gizzard.

Plant-eater teeth tell something about the size of the owner, but little about his shape and habits. Living animals show us that herbivores may be sleek and speedy like

The imperial elephant, an extinct Ice Age giant. The two middle nipper teeth became so large they are called tusks.

an antelope or big and awkward like a rhinoceros. The paleo-detective must wait for more evidence before he can know. He can, however, be fairly sure that they are peaceful beings, except for a few grouches such as the rhino and the wild hog. Whatever weapons they have are mainly for protection. A deer's antlers, for example, could well baffle an attacking wolf and might hurt it. But a deer will not usually attack another animal.

Some animals will eat almost anything and for that reason are known as omnivores. Man is one of them. Others are apes and bears. Men and bears can handle either a meat or plant diet fairly well, but they can't handle either kind as well as the specialists. We eat meat, but would have a rough time with a bone such as the dog ate. We could eat a blade of grass, too, but only slowly. Our grinder teeth are too smooth to do the job quickly. A cow can grind it better and has extra stomachs to take care of the grass after it is swallowed.

If we wanted to get the marrow out of a bone, we would use a hammer or a bone saw. And this is important. Many of the animals that enjoy a wide diet also have wide talents. Quite a few of them can walk on their hind legs, freeing their front legs so that they can use their front feet as hands. Only man has enough brain power to invent the saw and hammer, but some of the apes might be taught to use them.

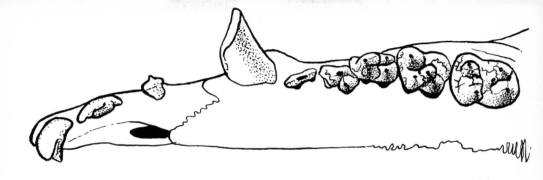

*Half view of the roof of a hog's mouth. The teeth are
not as sharp as those of the meat eaters, or as flat as
those of the plant eaters.*

As you would expect, the teeth of this omnivorous group
are in between the meat-eater teeth and the plant-eater
teeth. The front teeth are about the same size as the rest.
Sometimes the canine teeth are large, as in the case of the
bear. It needs the stabbers for defense and sometimes for
killing. The side teeth, or premolars, are not as scissorlike
as the dog's carnassials are; and although there are small
bumps on the back teeth, they are not as jagged as the
dog's back teeth, nor as rasplike as the cow's. From front
to back the teeth may be about the same size. An animal
that has all four kinds of teeth of about the same size is
likely to be among the more versatile ones. This is the kind
of teeth man has.

Some animals, such as birds, have no teeth at all. Birds
eat a wide variety of things—seeds, worms, bugs, fish, meat,
nectar. Most of these can be swallowed without chewing.

Pelicans and cormorants can swallow remarkably large fish without any trouble. Meat-eating birds, such as eagles and hawks, have heavy hooked beaks for tearing chunks from carcasses they hold with their sharp talons. The oldest fossil birds had teeth, but modern birds have lost theirs, and, instead, their jaws are covered with horny beaks. The beak is lighter and does the food-getting job just as well. Birds have gizzards and also have very strong digestive juices. They can digest large amounts of food in a short time, even though it may be in big chunks. This helps them to get along without scissor teeth, crushers or grinders.

A few four-footed animals have beaks instead of teeth. Turtles have them, and so did some of the dinosaurs. A few animals have neither. The anteater, for example. It licks up ants with its long, slender tongue and swallows them.

Life would be much easier for the paleontologist if all animals fit into the four groups described: carnivores, herbivores, omnivores, and the toothless ones, or the eden-tates. But a great many are in between. An example is the aardvark, a termite eater. It has a few teeth, so it cannot be called toothless. Some animals have teeth that are not at all like those of any of the simple groups. Certain rep-tiles have a great many sharp, needlelike teeth. Besides having them in the usual place, along the jaws, some have teeth in the roof of the mouth. Perhaps this is to keep wriggling items of diet from backing out.

Paleontologists prepare themselves for their work by studying all present-day animals as well as all of the extinct forms that have been found. With this background they are able to interpret newly discovered forms. Teeth differ so much from one kind of animal to another that a single tooth is sometimes enough to identify an animal. Take the horses, for example. They include a complete range from the tiny four-toed horses that lived millions of years ago, up to the big horses of today. All of these have been studied thoroughly and are well known. If you should take a horse tooth to a paleontologist he would look very closely at the grinding surface. He would examine the pattern of hard ridges on top and the grooves down the sides. He might measure the size. Finally, he could tell you how big the horse was, how many toes it had and how long ago it lived. He could tell you the name of that kind of horse, such as *Hyracotherium, Merychippus* or *Equus*. He might not be able to tell all these things from a whole armload of ribs or a dozen vertebrae, but from a single tooth, he could.

U. S. 1169349

35

SECOND, STUDY THE FEET

AFTER THE TEETH, the next clue to check out is the animal's feet and limbs, both front and hind. The paleo-detective knows that some kinds of feet are for walking, some for swimming, some for digging and some for other uses. When he has found out how his subject moved around, he has made a big step, himself. Knowing what the animal ate and how it moved, he can reason out a number of things about how it must have looked and behaved.

The first vertebrates that walked on land were built quite like salamanders. (A salamander is a slimy little lizard-shaped animal that lives in wet spots and seldom comes out into the open.) The early vertebrates had an awkward leg arrangement like this:

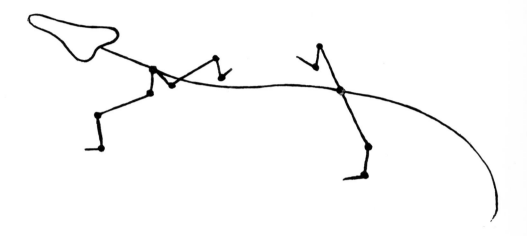

Awkwardness does not often go with efficiency, and these early walking animals were not exceptions. The feet were too far out from the body to give good support. Walking must have put quite a strain on the muscles, and the body probably dragged on the ground part of the time. The animal must have rested often, with its body lying flat on the ground. The stubby-toed feet served as little more than pads.

As animal life developed into higher forms, one of the big improvements was a change in the leg arrangement.

The hind limbs swung forward alongside the body, and the front swung back, like this:

A paleontologist can tell which of these two positions an animal's limbs were in by the way the thighbone fits into the hipbone and the upper arm into the shoulder.

With its limbs in this new position the animal was able to put some spring in his step. It lifted its body off the ground and carried it along, instead of dragging it. It is thought that warm blood was made possible when the body was freed from constant contact with the cold earth. Cold-blooded animals such as snakes and lizards get sluggish when they are cold and cannot protect themselves very well. Warm-blooded animals—man is one—can go into action quickly under wider weather conditions.

The kind of foot that developed with the new body position was more like our own. It had longer toes than the stubs of the earlier form, and the toes lay side by side, instead of fanning out from the ankle. The front and hind feet were much alike. With feet of this kind, the animal could move freely and might even have been a pretty good runner.

This was the first walking foot that really worked. It is the basic foot. The rest of the feet that will be described have come from it. Some have developed from it as dry-land feet, some as feet for animals that have gone back to the water. Others have developed for use in the trees and the air, while still others have developed for use under-ground.

Man's hind foot is much like the early walking foot, but his front foot has changed. In our case, the entire hind foot rests on the ground, enabling us to balance on two

Foot bones of a raccoon. Animals such as this walk as we do, with the sole of the foot on the ground.

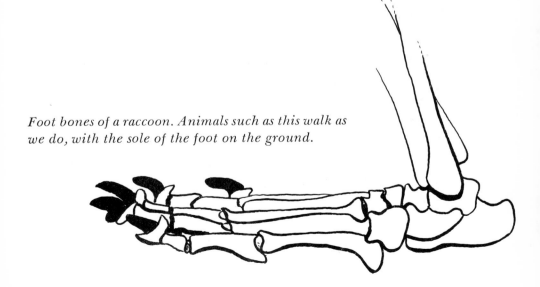

feet. This has freed our front feet from walking duty and has let them develop into hands. Really, a hand is not very different from a foot. Compare your own hand and foot. The foot has a bony heel that the hand doesn't have. Aside from that, the main difference is in the length and motion of the fingers and toes. Fingers are longer than toes, and you can move them better. But the motion is largely a matter of training. People who have lost the use of their arms have taught themselves to write with their toes, pick things up, and do most of the things we do with our fingers. The one thing the big toe cannot do is bend around for grasping. You can easily touch the tip of any finger with your thumb. That is how you get a good grip. The thumb is said to be "apposable," and this apposable thumb is the greatest difference between the hand and foot.

There is a belief that man's intelligence stems from his apposable thumb. Unlike most animals, early man could pick things up. Holding things in his hand, he looked at them more closely. He examined and felt them. He felt their weight, as no horse or cat could do, and he wondered about them. He became curious and began to learn.

Sooner or later he found he could throw, and that was an important discovery. It gave him a weapon no other animal had. He could hunt down his meat in a shorter time than before, and defend himself while his enemies were still at a distance. The easier life gave him more time

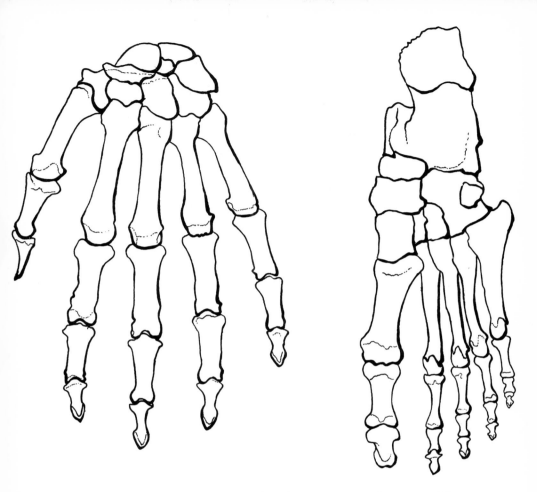

Hand and foot bones of man. The main differences are the apposable thumb and the heel, which is an enlarged foot bone.

to think. It is this thinking that places man on a different plane from all other animals.

The spectral tarsier has grasping hands and feet.

It is not true that all animals with apposable thumbs are smart. Some pretty stupid-looking and stupid-acting creatures have them. Spectral tarsiers, for example.

But when the paleo-detective finds a fossil animal that has a flat hind foot and a well-developed hand, he knows it is probably one that was well advanced. He can be fairly sure it could not run as fast as a deer, but that it got around very well. Probably it was not fast enough to overtake and kill other animals for a steady diet. In fact, it may not have been a meat eater at all. It could have been a fish- and berry-eating omnivore, like the bear. These possibilities must be kept in mind until other evidence points one way or the other.

Faster runners developed the toe-and-pad foot. It is the style we find in the dog and cat and their close relatives. It differs from the walking foot in its proportions and the way it is used. The toes and fingers are shorter and the palm bones much longer. The heel is up off the ground when the animal is walking or running. In fact, we don't think of it as a heel at all, because it doesn't touch the ground until the animal sits or lies down. Your own foot would be much like this if it were narrower and longer. When you walk on tiptoe you are using your foot in the same way this group normally walks. It is also what you do when you run.

Pads and claws generally go with this kind of foot. The

The cat walks on its toes with the claws curled up into protecting sheaths.

pads make a good contact with the ground and prevent slipping. For this purpose they are about as good as rubber-soled shoes and as quiet, which is important to a hunter.

All members of the cat family (and this includes lions, tigers and pumas as well as pet tabby cats) can protect their claws by withdrawing them into sheaths. The one exception is the cheetah, an animal living in parts of Asia and Africa. It has claws more like those of the dog. When claws are sheathed, they do not touch the ground. If they touched at every step they would soon be dull, or they might get broken. A mountain lion, or puma, kills by dropping on its prey from a tree. It spreads its toes, unsheathes its claws, and hangs on until it has broken its victim's neck with its jaws. Dull or broken claws could be a matter of life or death to an animal that depends on its claws for getting food.

The toe-and-pad foot is almost always found in the same skeleton with meat-eater teeth. If the claws are sharp and can be retracted into sheaths, the scientist is quite sure he has one of the cat family. He can assume that this one, like the rest of the cats, was a very fast runner for short distances. It overtook its food or dropped on it for the kill.

If the claws are not retractable, then the toe-and-pad animal must have been more like the dog. Dogs and wolves and their relatives generally are strong runners for long distances. They cannot overtake an antelope in a sprint,

Foot bones of a tapir (top), dog (middle) and bear (bottom). The tapir walks on its tiptoes, the dog on its toes, and the bear on its soles.

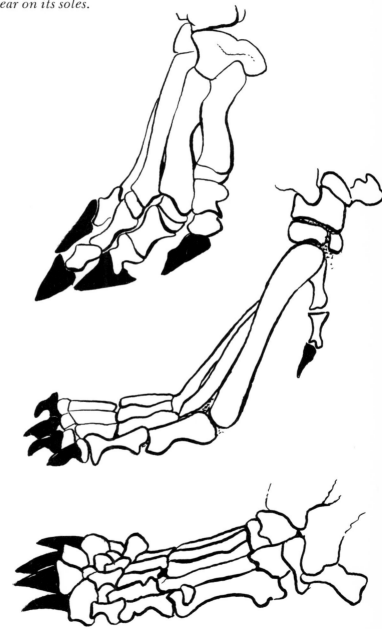

but they can keep chasing it until it can run no farther. When it gives out, the hunter has its meal.

The feet of the fastest runners are hoofed. Originally, the same bones were in the hoofed foot as in the toe-and-pad foot. The modern members of the group have lost all of the finger and toe bones except the middle one or two. Those that are left are so large and strong they could easily be taken for leg bones.

While the toe-and-pad animal is on its toes, the hoofed one is on its toenails, for a hoof is simply an enlarged nail.

The history of the horse shows that the change in the number of toes has taken place over millions of years. The earliest horse that has been found as a fossil was a little fellow about the size of a fox terrier. It is known to paleontologists as *Hyracotherium*, but most people call it *Eohippus*, from the Greek meaning "dawn horse." It had four toes on the front foot and three on the hind foot. Probably its ancestors had five toes on each foot, but this is not known for sure, because their fossil remains have not yet been found.

The next later kind of horse was a little larger, and it had three toes on each foot. The middle toe, or third digit, was by far the largest, and apparently carried most of the weight of the horse's body. This horse is known as *Miohippus. Merychippus,* a still later form, had an even larger middle toe. The side toes must have been of little use,

46

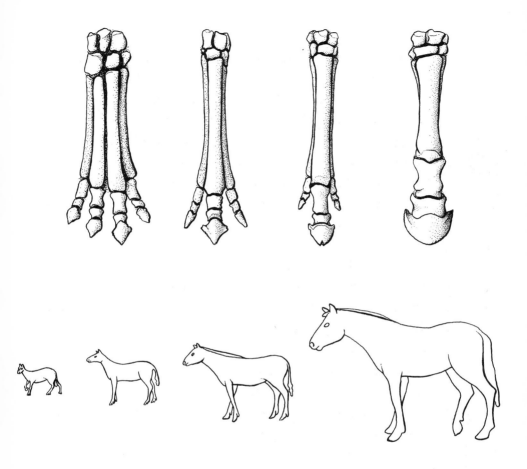

These drawings show the history of the horse and the development of its foot. Tiny Hyracotherium *lived some 60 million years ago; the next larger,* Miohippus, *was alive about 35 million years ago;* Merychippus *lived some 15 million years later; and* Equus, *the largest, is alive today.*

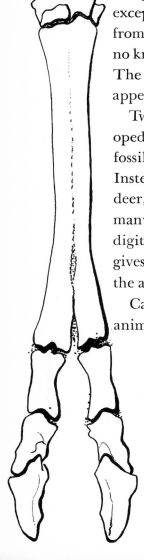

because they were quite small. In fact, they may have been of no use at all. They were so slight that they must have been broken easily. *Merychippus* was larger than earlier horses, but not nearly as large as modern horses.

Equus, the horse of today, has lost all of the side toes except a little sliver called the splint bone. A million years from now that, too, may be gone. The splint bone serves no known purpose and only causes trouble, when it breaks. The horse will be better off when this little bone has disappeared.

Two-hoofed, or "cloven-hoofed," animals have developed in the same way. As you go farther back into the fossil record, you find more toes, up to the original five. Instead of retaining only one toe on each foot, the cow, deer, antelope, hog, and many others, have kept two. In many cases, the long palm bones of the third and fourth digits (or toes) have grown solidly together, or fused. This gives greater strength than two separate bones. It also gives the appearance of a single toe with two hoofs.

Camels and caribou are not easily recognized as hoofed animals at all. The little hoofs of the camel are hidden in

Foot bones of a deer. The foot is made of the third and fourth toes, partly fused together.

its big, tough pads. The pads are much better for walking on the desert sand. The caribou has a special problem of walking in the swampy ground where it finds much of its food. It gets along quite well because its hoofs have spread out to make broad supports. It is almost as if it were wearing snowshoes.

Hoofed feet belong to the pursued, not the pursuer. A hunting animal would get nowhere stalking its prey on clattering hoofs. But the hoofed animal can defend itself pretty well by kicking and slashing at its attackers. Many of the cloven-hoofed animals also have horns or antlers for defense and fighting among themselves. Hoofs generally go with a plant diet, although a few of the hoofed animals, such as the hog, will eat anything. The greater number of these animals are very good runners up to a point. They are the "middle-distance" runners, compared with the sprinters and long-distance runners. Even the hog, in its wild state, can get up a fair speed.

When the paleo-detective finds hoofed feet he knows that he probably has a victim rather than a villain. But he needs more evidence before he can know whether it was fleet and trim like an antelope, slow and dignified like a camel, or pudgy like a pig.

These three are the main kinds of feet found in the animals that live on the earth's surface. Feet vary a good deal within each kind. One animal may have longer or wider feet than another. This shows a difference in the way the feet are used. Some animals, such as the impala, rabbit and kangaroo, leap or jump as much as they walk. The impala has cloven hoofs, while the others have hoofs more on the order of the toe and pad. Small changes in the shapes of the bones will tell the paleontologist that these are jumpers. He must be alert to these small things if he wants to learn the most from the fossils.

Four-footed animals that live in the trees have feet that are well suited to that purpose. Monkeys, for example, have hands that are about like ours. Their hind feet are similar to ours except for one thing: the big toe is apposable. As they swing about in the trees—or in their cages— monkeys are able to grasp just as firmly with the hind feet as with the hands. The big toe is almost like a thumb. With this kind of equipment, a monkey or a lemur can move about in the trees with little chance of falling to the ground. Falling is one of the worst things that can happen to a tree dweller.

Another type of tree-dweller foot belongs to the sloth. The unusual thing about it is the shape and size of the claws. They are long and strong and are curved to form hooks. When sleeping time comes, the sloth hooks its claws over the branch of a tree and relaxes in a dangling position. The curved claws clamp tight to the branch, and the sloth can go to sleep without worrying about falling. When the

A tree sloth. This South American tree dweller hooks its feet over tree limbs. It cannot straighten its toes.

sloth travels, it goes mainly in the upside-down position, too. Its unusual equipment serves it well in the trees. But it is something of a handicap when the sloth comes down to the ground. Its long claws get in the way so that it cannot set its foot down flat, and it has to walk on the sides of its feet. This gives it an awkward, rolling gait.

Many centuries ago, some of the tree sloths did come down to the ground to live in spite of this handicap, and took up cave dwelling. At least, skeletons of this type are found in cave rubble along with those of other animals that normally were cave dwellers. With their slow, lumbering walk, ground sloths could not have traveled far from their caves. And they probably had few worries about other animals attacking them. A good swipe with those claws should have discouraged any unfriendly neighbors. The claws were also good implements for log rolling and digging. The ground sloths probably lived on what they could dig up and on vegetation that grew nearby. There is evidence that they ate yucca leaves. Yucca leaves are so

The rat foot (left) and bat wing (right) are built on the same general plan.

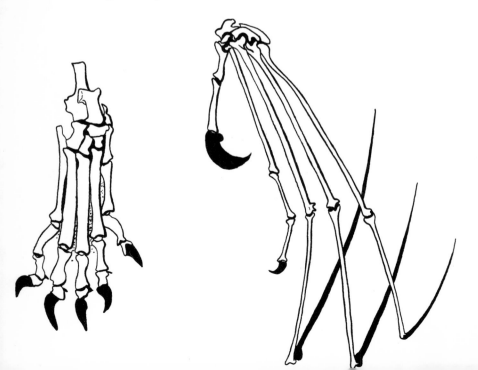

tough and stringy that no present-day animal will try to eat them. The ground sloth must have been very hardy in many ways, but nevertheless it is extinct.

The next step upward from tree-dwelling is flight. The flier most like the ground dwellers is the bat. It is so much like a mouse that its German name is *Fledermaus*, which means "flying mouse." The bat's wing is merely a hand with very long fingers and a thin skin stretched between them.

Bird wings are not much different from bat wings. The forearm bones are more important, and the fingers are shorter than in the bat. Only three fingers remain in the bird, and they have fewer joints than bat fingers have. The finger bones and forearm bones support the main feather quills.

When the paleontologist finds a fossil with wings he can be sure the animal was able to fly, unless the wings are too small. Some birds, such as the emu and ostrich, have such small wings in proportion to their bodies that they could not possibly fly with them.

Another odd bird is the penguin. Its wings are much too small for flight, and its legs are not for running. It waddles. The truth is that the penguin does fly, but it

In the bird wing some bones are fused and some are enlarged to anchor the feathers.

does it underwater. The wings of birds that fly in the air must be large enough to support their entire body weight. But this is no problem to the penguin. Underwater it has little weight, so all its wings have to do is give forward motion to a beautifully streamlined body. It can fly through the water very well with wings much too small to carry it in the air.

The hind feet of birds give additional information. There are differences in the feet and limbs of the wading birds, the paddlers and the birds of prey. The flamingo has long, slender legs, so it can wade through water searching for its food. The ducks have short, stubby legs, with webbed feet, so they can swim and dive quickly. And the eagle has strong legs with curved talons, or claws, to seize and hold its food.

Several animals returned to a life in the water after developing into four-footed land animals. Such an animal is the sea lion. The sea lion is the one that balances a ball on its nose and is billed as the trained seal in circuses and animal shows.

The sea lion is still a land animal to some extent. It spends some of its time lolling about on sandy beaches or rocks. It can still walk, but no one would call it a very graceful walk. In the water it swims rapidly and gracefully. Its leg bones follow the same pattern as that which is found in the common land animals. Its arm and leg bones are

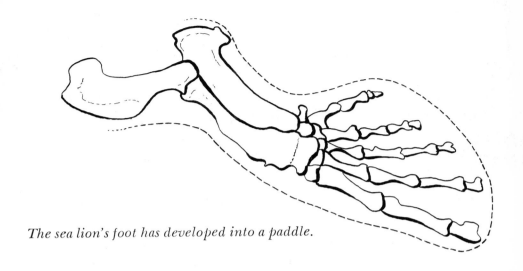

The sea lion's foot has developed into a paddle.

short and heavy, and form powerful flipper stalks. The hand and foot bones are long, with the fingers and toes fairly well spread, to form broad flippers. The foot is streamlined for underwater use and is very successful. Water-living animals with feet like these have been on earth since early geologic time. Some of the extinct animals, such as the ichthyosaurs, plesiosaurs and mosasaurs, had good paddle feet.

In addition to the animals that live on the land, in the trees or in the water, there are some that live in the earth. They are well suited to that life. One of the most interest-

Extinct paddle-footed reptiles. © FMNH, drawn by Chas. R. Knight

ing of these is the mole. You seldom see it, because it spends almost its entire life underground. It doesn't see you, either, because it has practically lost its sight. Probably it can only tell daylight from dark with its tiny eyes. Where it lives, there is almost no light to see by, so it has little use for eyes.

If your arms were built according to the mole's plan, they would be about half as long as they are. The bones would be heavier, and your hands would be about the size and shape of a fielder's mitt—maybe even bigger. Your fingernails would be even larger in proportion. And your shoulder muscles would be bigger and stronger than those of any wrestler who ever lived.

The mole, of course, is a tiny fellow. It's not much more than six or seven inches long. All its life it digs its way through the soil with its powerful digging hands. Its food is the worms and bugs it finds. It likes to tunnel in through the rich soil around people's favorite garden plants, because there its food is plentiful. No doubt you have seen its burrows crossing a yard, particularly if the ground is soft and moist. For this life of digging, its equipment is ideal. The mole is no problem for the paleontologist to identify. The combination of small size, short, heavy arms, and spadelike hands can point only to a digger.

One of nature's laws is that animal life spreads out into all kinds of places where life can exist. Changes in the body structure and habits of the animals gradually take place to fit them to live in their particular places. The many kinds of feet represent such changes. For this reason, feet are good clues to the animal's life and surroundings.

The mole has heavy, knobby armbones, and spade-like hands designed for digging.

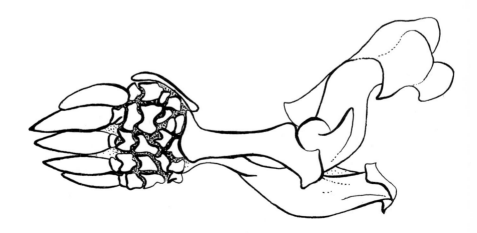

THEN, SEARCH FOR MORE FACTS

BESIDES THE TEETH and feet
there are a great many other clues to an animal's life and
habits. One who studies fossils must be looking for all of
them. Like the detective, he must not miss a single clue or
he may arrive at the wrong answer.

The shape of each bone in the skeleton has meaning,
because the shape reflects the use to which the bone is put.
That is, a bone that carries a heavy weight must be a sturdy
bone, while a light-duty bone may be slender. If the muscles place a great strain on a bone it must be strong. Each
bone shows, by its shape, which muscles attached to it were
the most important. At the place where the most important
muscles were attached, the bone is likely to be broadened,
or to have a ridge.

Roughness of the bone is another useful clue. Bones
generally are quite smooth except where muscles are attached. As an embryo develops into an infant, the bones

and muscles "grow up" together, connected by strong tendon or gristle. The surface of the bone is rough where the tendon is attached so that the bond between them will be strong. When the muscle and tendon have decayed and only the fossil bone is found, the scarred and pitted surface shows where the muscle was attached.

A person who knows muscles and bones can learn a great deal from the shapes of various bones, and the location of the muscle scars. He might, for example, examine a set of forearm bones and say, "This animal must have had better than average strength in its arms because the bones are thick for their length. The large knob at the elbow shows that there was a large muscle for straightening the arm. There is also a scarred and broadened area where the arm-bending muscle comes down from the shoulder. This means that the arm-bending muscle was strong and important."

Such is the situation in the mole. Its entire arm skeleton is made up of short, thick bones with many bumps and knobs and muscle scars where the powerful digging muscles are attached. Its leg bones, however, are not as heavy and do not have large bumps. The hind feet are used chiefly in moving loose dirt out of the way, so the muscles are not as big and bumps on the bones are not needed.

In some animals certain muscles are so large that high ridges of bone are needed as attachment areas. The duck is an example. It flies to find food, and it flies to escape danger. It can fly for hours without pause. Flying means life itself, and its flight muscles are the largest of all. They run from the breastbone, or sternum, out to the wings. A high ridge, known as the keel, runs down the middle of the sternum and has muscles for the right wing attached to one side and those for the left wing on the other.

In contrast, an emu does not fly at all. The keel on its sternum is not nearly as high as that of the duck. All of the studies of wild birds have shown that the strong fliers have a high keel on the sternum.

The gorilla has a similar ridge along the top of its skull from front to back. In this case, the ridge is called a crest. The muscles that operate the massive jaws are attached to it. Such a crest is found only in the animals with unusual power in their jaws.

When a paleontologist is studying an unknown fossil skeleton, he goes over each bone very carefully looking for knobs, bumps and ridges, which he calls protuberances. The shapes of the bones tell him which muscles were important. Since he knows what each muscle does, he is able to tell what movements the animal made, and to judge which ones were most important. He knows, then, a great deal more about how the animal lived and acted.

Suppose he is studying a skeleton that has small, smooth armbones and big leg bones with some scars and bumps.

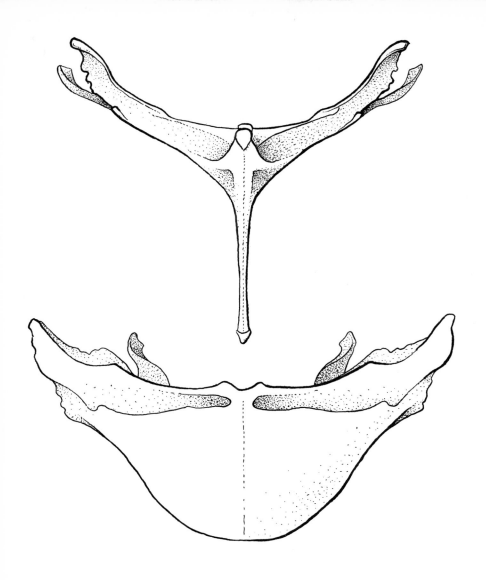

The wild duck (top) has a great keel to anchor the powerful flight muscles. The ostrich (bottom), which does not fly, has no keel.

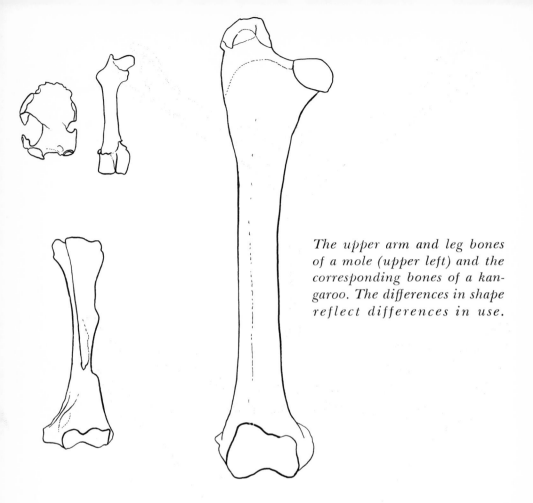

The upper arm and leg bones of a mole (upper left) and the corresponding bones of a kangaroo. The differences in shape reflect differences in use.

This animal couldn't have been anything like a mole. It is the opposite so far as the limbs are concerned. Bumps and scars show that the big muscles were connected to the hind limbs. One set of muscles was the largest by far, the one that straightens out the hind legs. With this equipment, the animal could not have been a digger. It isn't likely to have been a strong swimmer, because all the strong swimmers we know about have their power in the front limbs. It is easy to tell that it didn't have wings and couldn't fly. If it had been a tree dweller that swung from branch to branch, the front limbs would be long. Probably it didn't even travel on all four feet, or the limbs would be nearly equal in size. Most likely, then, it was a jumper. So the scientist says to himself, "This probably will turn out to be much like a kangaroo," and goes ahead to sift other evidence.

Thickness of bone is another clue to check out. In general, heavy, lumbering animals have heavy, thick bones. Most of the light, quick, active animals have light, slender bones. Compare the forearm bones of a monkey with those of a rhinoceros. Certainly the monkey would have a hard time among the branches with anything like rhino bones. And the rhino would be no better off depending on little monkey bones to carry its weight.

The flying birds have even lighter bones than the monkey. Instead of having marrow in the middle, the bones are hollow. Light weight is more important to a bird than to most animals, because it can't stop in mid-air to rest its muscles. At the same time, the frame must be strong. The hollow bones give strength without great weight. In fact, bird bone is one of the strongest things for its weight in the animal kingdom.

Forearm bones of a monkey (left) and a rhinoceros.

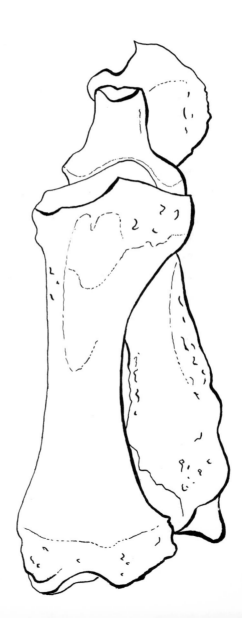

Birds are the only present-day animals that have hollow bones. Some of the lightweight, active dinosaurs also had them. This fact is one of the bits of evidence pointing to a family relationship between the dinosaurs and birds.

Something unusual about hollow bones can be found in some birds. In ducks, for example, the lungs extend into the hollow wing bones. If fuel tanks in airplane wings make sense, this does, too. Both arrangements make use of space that might otherwise be wasted.

You are acquainted with a few animals that have armor—the turtle, for example, and perhaps you have seen an armadillo. The fossil glyptodont was similar to the armadillo but much larger. Another armored animal from the distant past is the odd-looking *Stegosaurus*, which carried a picket fence in its back.

These armored animals have a few things in common. First, they are slow, because their armor weighs them down. Second, since they do move so slowly, they are not the hunting type—at least, they don't hunt anything speedier than worms or sluggish beetles. Mainly, they are vegetable eaters and are very placid. When trouble comes along, they meet it by retiring into their shells, or by rolling up like a pill bug. When the danger has passed, they go on about their business. Some armored animals live on the land and some in the water. A few, such as the turtle, can live either place.

Stegosaurus, *an armored dinosaur that lived 170 million years ago.*   © FMNH, drawn by Chas. R. Knight

Once in a while the paleontologist calls in a doctor. He may find strong evidence that some of the fossil bones were diseased. An osteologist, a doctor who has made a special study of bones and their diseases, may be able to tell what the disease was and, perhaps, what caused it. This adds a little more to human knowledge. Fossils sometimes show that broken bones have healed, but not often. A broken bone is a more serious handicap to a wild animal than it is to a civilized human. A break may slow the animal down enough so that it will fail to catch its food, or fail to get away from a pursuer. In either case, the animal is likely to die before the break has a chance to heal.

The questions about fossil animals have not all been answered. Sometimes a paleo-detective finds a clue that he cannot understand. The pelycosaurs, for example, were land animals that lived millions of years ago. Why did several of them have sails on their backs? At least, they look more like sails than anything else. A land animal hasn't much use for a sail, so these must have been for some other purpose. Two or three generations of scientists have puzzled over this. The best explanation so far is that the sail served as a sort of solar heating system for the cold-blooded animal. When the sun shone on this expanse of skin, it could have warmed the blood stream quickly. But without nerves and blood vessels, which are seldom found in fossils, it is hard to tell whether this is the right answer. It is just the most intelligent guess at the present.

You now have some idea of the kinds of things a paleontologist looks for among the bones. You know why he is

The pelycosaur, a reptile that lived in Texas 250 million years ago.

interested in teeth as a clue to diet. You know the limbs will tell how the animal moved, and that, in turn, will give information about its surroundings. They will show whether it lived on land, in the water, underground, in the trees or in the air. Bone ridges, scars and bumps will show which muscles were largest and most important. Heaviness or lightness of bone is important. Then, the presence or absence of armor, sails and other oddities adds a little more to the story.

These are only the simplest things in the life of the paleontologist. As he works with fossils, he keeps learning more and more about them. He knows better what to look for as he comes across each new specimen. Sometimes small points that might easily be overlooked turn out to be of very great importance.

Three stories—about the Mount Shasta bison, an early bird and a dinosaur—will show how scientists have used all of these principles to solve three problems in identifying and restoring the fossil remains of animals now extinct.

CASE HISTORIES

THE SHASTA BISON

Seldom does a paleo-detective find a problem as simple as the Case of the Shasta Bison. It was easy, but it was interesting, too, because this proved to be one of the largest bison ever found. It was a close relative of the American bison, commonly known as the buffalo.

One winter day in 1933, Burnett Day was helping his father "work the sheep" near the base of Mount Shasta in California. The sheep were warm in their thick wool coats, but Burnett was cold. He wanted to get home. As he followed the sheep up the trail he tossed pebbles at the tails of the laggards. It helped hurry them a little.

Burnett stooped over to pick up an odd-shaped pebble from the bank along the trail. It stuck fast. He tugged at it a moment and then looked more closely. This bank was mostly loose sand with some gravel in it. Anything as small as a pebble should come out easily, but this object seemed to be rooted deeply. He scraped a bit of sand from around it and found it looked like a cow's horn. He tugged again with no better result. Curious, he dug and tugged until he was sure it was actually a horn. Yet, it looked like a rock. How could a thing like this happen? This was no place to bury a cow! It must be something else—but what?

Burnett skipped after the sheep and hurried them along home, so he could ask his father to come and see the horn-shaped rock. Back on the sheep trail, they both scraped more sand away. "This is no ordinary cow's horn," exclaimed Mr. Day. "If it belonged to a cow at all it must have been Babe, the Blue Ox. We shouldn't fool with it because it might be something important. We'll pull the sand up around it so no one will notice it's been dug out, and then I'll see what I can find out about it."

Over the phone, the Chairman of the Paleontology Department at the University of California said it sounded like something that should be checked. So, the next day, lanky Dr. V. L. VanderHoof arrived on the spot with a collection of shovels, trowels, brushes, shellac and, most important, years of experience in identifying fossil bones. Ever so carefully, the Days and Dr. VanderHoof cleared the sand and gravel away from the horn. Close to the fossil they used trowels and brushes instead of shovels so they would not mar the bone. As each new bit of bone was cleared from the sand, they brushed shellac into it. Sometimes bones that have been buried a long time fall apart when they are exposed to air. Shellac protects them until they can be taken to the laboratory.

A few hours later eighteen inches of horn had been uncovered and a small crowd had gathered to watch. People wondered how a Texas longhorn had wandered into California. By the time the base of the horn was uncovered, they had stopped talking about cattle—even about Babe. The horn was three and a half feet long and seven inches in diameter!

"If you think that's big," said Van (no one called him Dr. VanderHoof any more), " you should have seen it in its original shape. This is only the core that we're digging up."

Horns of cows and bison are in two parts. The core in the center is hard and bony. The sheath, or covering around it, is more like the material in fingernails. It decays more quickly than the core and is not often preserved as a fossil.

The core was all that had been seen by most of the onlookers. Van himself saw more. He noticed that a layer of sand around the core was a little different in color from the rest. It also held together a little better. To Van this was clear evidence of the horn sheath, and he was filling his notebook with its description and measurements. By using plenty of shellac, he could even save parts of the sheath. Horn cores about the same size had been found before, but Van was sure that the sheaths were still unknown. Even if nothing was here but this one horn, it was still a find, because the sheath measurements would add a new bit to human knowledge.

Digging was hard work, but excitement was high. What was this huge animal? Was it all there, or just the horn? It took two days to find out. The skull was complete with both horn cores, lacking only a few small bits. Several cubic yards of sand and gravel were moved in the hope of finding the complete skeleton, but it wasn't there. Perhaps the rest of the bones had been scattered by meat-eating animals. Perhaps they had been washed away by the same storms that had covered the heavy skull with sand and gravel. Anyway, the enormous skull had been well worth the effort of digging.

Before the skull was completely uncovered, Van was fairly sure it was a bison, and a big one. But he waited until he had seen the teeth. He knew when he saw them that the animal had been a plant eater. This was to be expected, because horned animals are always plant eaters. But the details of the tooth pattern showed that it was not like a horse, a deer, an elephant, or any other animal except a bull or a bison. A bull's horns start out in one direction from the skull, while a bison's start out in an-

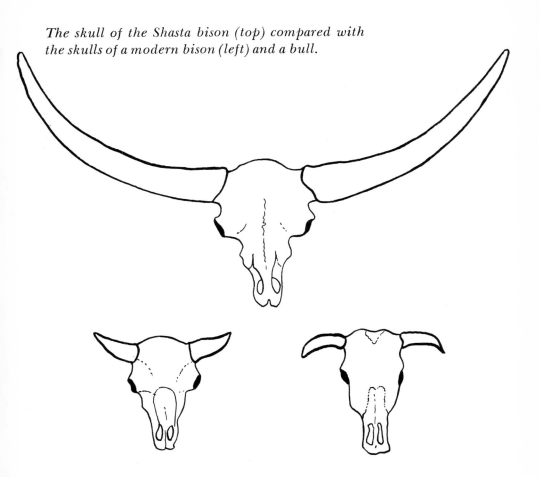

The skull of the Shasta bison (top) compared with the skulls of a modern bison (left) and a bull.

other. These horns went the way the bison's do. Besides, the forehead was broad and arched. All of the evidence pointed toward the bison. The only question was *which* bison.

Whenever an important fossil is found, some paleontologist studies it. He learns everything about it that he thinks is worth knowing. Then he writes a complete account of everything he has learned. He takes pictures and makes drawings, so that all of the details are on record. Generally, his museum or university publishes his description of the fossil and sends copies to all other scientific centers where the information might be useful.

Pieces of a few other skulls of this kind of giant bison had been found in other places. Part of Dr. VanderHoof's job, then, was to compare his fossil with the descriptions and pictures of all the others. The teeth of the Shasta bison were exactly like the pictures of all the fossils given the name of *Bison latifrons*. Measurements of the skull and the horn cores agreed closely. In fact, no difference of importance was found. So this skull was given the same name, *Bison latifrons*. "Latifrons" is a combination of Latin words meaning "broad front." Look at the picture of *Bison latifrons*, and you'll agree that it is well named.

The Shasta bison skull is the most complete of any *Bison latifrons* found so far. It is the only one with evidence of the shape of the entire horns. How easily that interesting information could have been lost! It would have been lost if less skill had been used in uncovering the horns.

Before Dr. VanderHoof was satisfied, he wanted to know the fossil still better—to see what it had looked like in the flesh. A large order, perhaps, but such things can be done.

One of the less-known professions is that of the paleo-sculptor. It is he who makes the models and life-size reconstructions from the fossil evidence. In this case, the paleo-sculptor was William G. Huff. He and Dr. Vander-Hoof pooled their knowledge and skill to rebuild the Shasta bison head in the shape it had had in life.

The first step was to make a plaster cast of the skull and horn cores. A plaster cast is a duplicate of the original fossil, but it is made of plaster of Paris. The making of a cast is a simple job unless the object is very large or its shape is complicated. First, the object is covered with plaster of Paris. When this has hardened, it is carefully cut away from the object into several sections. These are coated with paraffin on the inside surfaces and put back together to form a shell. The hollow inside the shell is the exact shape of the original object. Then the hollow is filled with more plaster of Paris, which is allowed to harden. The paraffin keeps the new plaster from sticking to the shell. The shell is taken apart again and removed, revealing a cast that is exactly the size and shape of the original object.

A plaster cast of the bison skull was not easy to make because the skull was so big. It was done in several sections that were later fitted together very carefully. The result was a duplicate of the original skull that could be used as a base for plaster muscles and coat.

With Dr. VanderHoof's measurements as a guide, Mr. Huff added to the plaster cast until the cores of the horns were covered to the same size and shape as those of the living animal. He put more plaster over the cast of the bony skull, building it up to look like the modern bison. Where bone ridges showed that certain cheek muscles must have been big, he built them up with more plaster. The final step was the fur coat. Fur is seldom preserved as fossil material. As fossils go, this one was not very old, so it was assumed that it looked much like the modern bison. Modern bison have wavy fur, and there is no evidence that *Bison latifrons* was different. Modern bison have wavy beards, so *Bison latifrons* probably had a wavy beard. Mr. Huff provided the wavy coat and beard by molding and shaping the plaster with various tools. Vertebrae found with some of the other skulls of the giant bison showed that it, like the modern relative, had a high shoulder hump. Now the Shasta bison was as complete as the fossil evidence would permit.

A little tug at a horn tip in the gravel led to a remarkable fossil head with a horn spread of seven feet. If the horns had been straight, the distance from tip to tip would have been almost twice as great. The body, to carry such a head in the normal bison position, would have had to be about eight feet high at the shoulders. The modern

*Reconstructed head of the giant bison. The horns
are seven and one-half feet across the curve.*

five-foot bison would look like a calf next to this giant.

The restoration was finished in time to be displayed at
the Golden Gate Exposition in 1939 and 1940. Many thousands of people saw it there and learned a little more about
the animal world of two hundred thousand years ago—all
because a boy tossed stones at some sheep and because a
scientist and a sculptor worked patiently together.

77

ARCHAEOPTERYX

ABOUT ONE HUNDRED AND
FORTY million years ago, two birds fell in the mud of a bay
ten miles apart and died. They probably didn't fall on the
same day—perhaps not even in the same century. We would
never have known about it, except for the fact that the bay
mud was a special, fine-grained kind that later hardened
to form lithographic limestone.

For many years, this kind of limestone has been used in
lithographic printing. Workers in the limestone quarries
in Bavaria had found fossil bones from time to time and
knew they could count on a little side money from their
sale. A little extra money was welcome, so these men were
always alert. It was a big day in the science of paleontology
when, in 1861, they split a slab and found not only bones,
but feather imprints. Sixteen years later the same thing
happened in another quarry, ten miles away.

Archaeopteryx, *the earliest-known bird. This is the original fossil after many years of cleaning.*

The first paleontologist to see the fossil remains could tell at a glance that these were of a very primitive feathered animal. He couldn't even be sure it was a bird because birds didn't have long bony tails, and this did. To be on the safe side, he named it from two Greek words meaning "primitive" and "feather"—*Archaeopteryx*. He added a second name to show that the animal was from the quarry.

The full name came out as *Archaeopteryx lithographica*. After years of study and many differences of opinion, scientists agree that the two birds are the same kind.

The first of the two birds was bought by the British Museum (Natural History) in London, and the second was given to the Museum of Natural History in Berlin. Several generations of scientists have studied them, each man adding a little information. During the years of study, methods have changed. The first men worked with chisels and scrapers and depended on their own eyesight. Hour after hour, a man would peck and scrape away at the limestone, not daring to scrape too close to the bone for fear he might scratch it. Even an inch from the bone he used care, because he never knew when he might come across another bone that was buried. These people cleaned up the main pieces so that the different bones could be recognized.

Later workers were able to do a cleaner and closer job, because they used binocular microscopes—double-barreled microscopes built for both eyes. Still later, it was found that X ray could be used on the rock slab. X-ray photographs showed where the buried bones were and gave their rough outlines. In very recent years, ultraviolet light has cleared up some questions as to where the bone ended and the rock began. This is possible because bone glows under ultraviolet light much more than limestone does.

Archaeopteryx was a puzzler, right from the first. Was

it a bird, or wasn't it? Birds weren't supposed to have long bony tails, of course; and these also had teeth! The brain case was more like that of a reptile than a bird. Was it a reptile that just happened to have feathers?

Most paleontologists believed then, as they do now, that birds descended from some line of small, light dinosaurs. These dinosaurs might have found it convenient to live in the trees. (Why not? There are tree lizards, tree toads and tree snakes.) It is thought that they learned to glide a little in jumping from branch to branch. In time, they could have learned to fly from tree to tree. At the same time, their scales may have become lighter and lighter, gradually fraying around the edges and finally developing into feathers. No one knows whether it happened that way. That is simply the most reasonable explanation suggested so far.

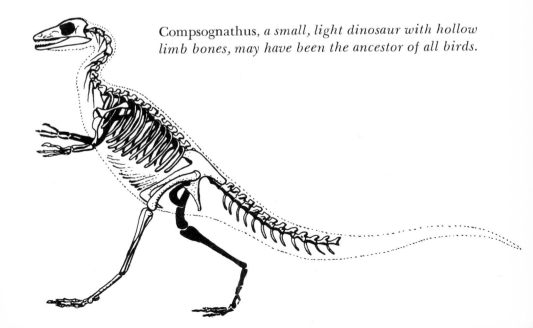

Compsognathus, *a small, light dinosaur with hollow limb bones, may have been the ancestor of all birds.*

If it is true that birds developed from reptiles, where would you draw the line between them? Did the animal become a bird when it began to glide? When it learned true flight? When its tail became short? When its teeth gave way to a beak? Paleontologists settled the point by agreeing on a simple rule: if it has feathers, it's a bird. *Archaeopteryx lithographica* had feathers; therefore, it was a bird. The important thing is that *Archaeopteryx* represents a stage between reptiles and birds as we know them.

Some scientist must have had a surprise when he looked for the beak of this feathered creature and, instead, he found teeth. As teeth go, they weren't much, but they did tell something about what the animal could have eaten. They were tiny peg-shaped things, not very close together. Their weakness ruled out the possibility of a meat or plant diet. These teeth couldn't have crushed seeds or helped in harvesting nectar. Neither were they the omnivore type. But they would have been handy for holding bugs or small fish. Until better information is at hand, it is agreed that *Archaeopteryx* probably ate insects and, perhaps, small fish. The fish diet would seem more likely if the bird had web feet, which is very doubtful.

The front feet in this creature were, of course, wings. They were much like today's chicken wings, except that they had claws. Perhaps the claws were useful and perhaps not. After all, this early bird's family had not lived in trees very many millions of years, and so it may have been clumsy. Hooks may have helped it. Or, like the horse's splint bone, perhaps the claws just hadn't disappeared yet.

Feathers are not solid enough to be preserved as fossils. They left their record, though, in the form of prints. The mud was so fine that imprints of single barbs can be made out in the rock. These prints show that the feathers were much like those on modern birds. Even the arrangement was about the same, except that there was no fan of tail feathers. Instead, a row of feathers bordered each side of the long bony tail.

In considering the hind legs, think of the two bones in a chicken drumstick. One is large, and the second tapers down to toothpick size. This difference in the size of the two bones holds true in all modern birds, but not in *Archaeopteryx*. They were about the same thickness and about the same length. In this way, it was more like a reptile than a bird.

The hind foot did have one feature that was very birdlike. The big toe pointed to the rear and was apposable. This made its foot quite like that of a hawk, which grasps small animals. With those tiny teeth, though, the early bird would not have been able to tear any small animals apart if it did catch them. So it seems more reasonable that *Archaeopteryx* used its clawed feet to perch on branches.

Hollow bones apparently had not yet developed at the

time these birds lived. The extra weight of marrow-filled bones must have been a handicap in flight; but it wasn't the only one. The breastbone, without a keel, shows that the muscles operating the wings were small and did not have much strength. All strong fliers have high keels on the sternum; so *Archaeopteryx*, with its keelless sternum, must have made short flights. Naturally, you would have expected the beginners to be weak. So far, the evidence all points to a primitive flying animal.

. Already, a fair picture of the animal is beginning to take shape, even though it is based only on the teeth and limbs and a quick look at the breastbone. Closer study will bring out more clues. For instance, the brain case is well enough preserved to show the primitive shape of the brain.

Except in the very simplest of animals, a brain has two general areas. The front part is where thinking takes place. The back part controls balance and the motions that we make without having to think. You breathe, and your heart beats, and one footstep follows another, without any thought on your part. You stay right side up without planning to do so. These are among the actions controlled by the hind part of the brain. Most of the things a bird does are the ones that come naturally, without any planning or reasoning. Probably that is why the modern bird has a much bigger hind brain than fore brain. The hind brain serves as a sort of automatic pilot and perhaps a navigator.

This was not true of *Archaeopteryx*. Both parts were small. Probably it wasn't able to do much thinking, and its flying wasn't very skillful. It must have flown like a student pilot compared to the captain of a jet liner.

The long tail fits in with this same thought. Imagine an airplane with a tail surface as long as a wing. The plane would be hard to control and sluggish. Rough weather could tear it apart. The long tail of *Archaeopteryx* must have had much the same effect. Undoubtedly, it was there simply because it hadn't yet shortened from the ancestral condition. When it finally did shorten to the present-day fantail, it was much more sensitive and reacted more quickly. Possibly the fall into the mud was caused by a mid-air breakup due to rough crosswinds. With the primitive tail and primitive brain, *Archaeopteryx* was not well fitted to cope with bad weather.

Archaeopteryx was not as secure against breakage as modern birds, for several reasons. First, a modern bird has branching ribs that are laced together by muscles, and hold its mid-frame together firmly. *Archaeopteryx* had slender ribs without any interlocking branches. Second, its verte-brae fitted together in the simplest possible way, with merely a round, end-to-end joint. Next time you eat chicken, notice how the vertebrae interlock for greater strength. At the same time they are lightweight. Third, the hipbone was fused to a sacrum of only six vertebrae. This was not as strong as the sacrum in modern birds, which includes a dozen or more vertebrae fused together.

All of these weaknesses must have made flying dangerous, and they must also have added to the hazard of landing. If this bird ever came in for a landing too fast, it would surely have broken something. This hazard has led some people to believe it may have landed by using its wing claws to hook onto the tree branches.

In spite of all these weaknesses, *Archaeopteryx* had a few structures besides its feathered wings that were better than its ancestors had. It had a strong furcula, or wishbone, where its reptile ancestors had two separate bones. And its hipbones were taking on the long, birdlike shape.

Perhaps some day all the bones of this primitive bird will be taken out of the rock slab, and the skeleton assembled in a lifelike position. This has not been done, even though skilled men have worked on the job, off and on, for almost a century. The main reason is that the bones cannot be taken out without ruining the feather imprints. In the meantime, several drawings and sculptures of the living bird have been made, and they all agree very well. Each of the artists had about the same store of information. He knew the sizes of all the bones. From these, he could tell that the bird was about the size of a chicken; and he could tell the lengths of the wings, legs and tail. He knew the shape of the feet, and was aware that there were claws on

Archaeopteryx, *restored.*

the fingers as well as the toes. He could see the teeth and
copy them correctly. Since the bird had no keel on the sternum, he must make it flat-chested, compared to a chicken.
He could use a present-day bird as a model for the feathers,

because the fossil showed no major difference except in the arrangement along the tail. The major missing item was an idea of the bird's color. Even here, he might make a reasonable guess. The varied colors of some modern birds could easily be a late development. It seems most reasonable that they developed from something less vivid, so it is assumed that *Archaeopteryx* would have been some neutral color.

What has the study of *Archaeopteryx lithographica* added to human knowledge? It has provided a clear guidepost that aids the thinking of those who are studying the relation of early animals to present forms.

Birds and reptiles have a number of points in common, such as the shape of the pelvis and the presence of scales (on the legs in the case of the bird). Scientists wondered if they might be related. Then the fossil remains of flying reptiles were found, and the wondering became a belief. Still, the evidence was not strong because the flying reptiles were not much like birds. They had batlike wings, and no evidence of feathers was found.

With the finding of *Archaeopteryx* little room was left for doubt. This animal had a long, reptilelike tail, reptilelike teeth, a reptilelike brain, and claws on its fingers. Yet, it had feathers and the shape of a bird. Here was the "missing link" providing strong evidence that birds and reptiles are related.

THE FRILLED DINOSAUR

Explorer Roy Chapman Andrews halted the caravan of cars near the Flaming Cliffs of Mongolia. For a hundred miles the Central Asiatic Expedition had not met a living person. Now a small cluster of tentlike homes showed in the distance. It was always a good idea to stop and talk to the Mongols, because they knew which were the better trails to follow. Much more important, they often knew where the pirates of the desert had been waylaying caravans. The expedition wasn't there to fight brigands, though it could do it if it had to. It was in Asia to collect fossils and gather other scientific information.

J. B. Shackelford was the photographer for the expedition, and a good one, but he had another talent. It was said that he could smell a fossil a hundred million years away. Like the rest of the explorers, he could not rest when there was a nearby cliff that might have fossils. "Shack" walked over to the Flaming Cliffs to spend five minutes prospecting and then hurry back to the caravan before it started on its way. He did hurry back, but not because the cars were getting ready to move on. He was carrying what was to be one of the most important fossil discoveries in many years —the first skull of *Protoceratops andrewsi*.

Even Walter Granger, the expedition's chief paleontologist, had never seen a skull just like this one. What was more, he was pretty sure no one else had, either. Granger could tell that it belonged to a reptile and that certain things about it were like the horned ceratopsian dinosaurs. But it had no horns.

The ceratopsian dinosaurs were a group of lumbering beasts that are known from the fossil records of Wyoming, Montana and some other states, as well as from Mongolia. The word ceratopsian comes from two Greek words, "keras" and "opsis," meaning "horn" and "eye." A cera-

Reconstructions. Triceratops *(left), presumed to be descended from* Protoceratops, *is attacked by* Tyrannosaurus *(right).*

© FMNH, drawn by Chas. R. Knight

topsian had horns over the eyes. The well-known *Tricera-tops* was one of the ceratopsian dinosuars. It had a horn over each eye, and one on the nose. *Triceratops* also had a big bony covering over the neck. During the millions of years that the ceratopsian dinosaurs lived on earth, they changed and developed as the horse did. The early ceratopsians were much smaller than those that lived thousands of years later. Also, the horn arrangements were less complicated. So it seems reasonable to believe the ancestors of these animals were still smaller and hornless. Granger thought the skull found at the Flaming Cliffs was this ancestor.

A collecting party has no time to clean and study the fossils it finds. That is a laboratory job. Instead, the men pack their specimens and ship them back to headquarters. That is what happened to the skull that Shackelford found. The next year a message came from the American Museum of Natural History saying that the animal was new to science. It was given the name *Protoceratops,* or "early ceratopsian." The rest of the name — *andrewsi* — was in honor of Dr. Andrews, the expedition's leader.

A single skull doesn't tell everything scientists want to know about an extinct animal. Shackelford's find merely excited new curiosity about the ancestral ceratopsian. More evidence must be found, if it existed.

The expedition was homeward bound when it stopped

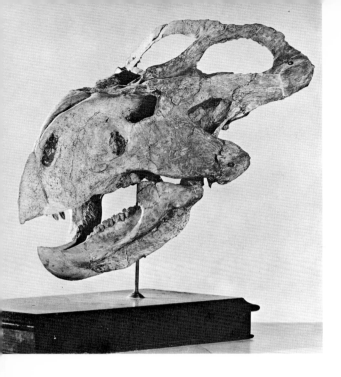

Skull of the earliest-known horned dinosaur, Protoceratops.

at the Flaming Cliffs. The 1922 collecting season was over. But the men all agreed the Flaming Cliffs would be the first stop when they explored central Asia again in 1923. If necessary, the men would search the cliffs with a fine-tooth comb to find more clues. As it turned out, a hay rake would have been good enough. About seventy-five skulls were sent back to the American Museum in 1923. Several skeletons were found, too, complete to the small bones of the tail.

In almost a century, all that has been found of *Archaeopteryx* is two skeletons and a feather; but in Mongolia a complete age series of *Protoceratops* was found in one collecting season plus one day. All ages of *Protoceratops* were there, from newly hatched youngsters to old granddaddies. For the first time, scientists could trace the growth of a dinosaur from babyhood to old age.

All of this was big news to paleontologists, but most people would never have read of *Protoceratops* in their newspapers if it had not been for George Olsen. He found eggs.

But DINOSAUR eggs!

Dinosaur eggs were in newspaper headlines all over the world. The idea of seventy-five-million-year-old eggs caught

Egg and skulls representing four growth stages of Protoceratops.

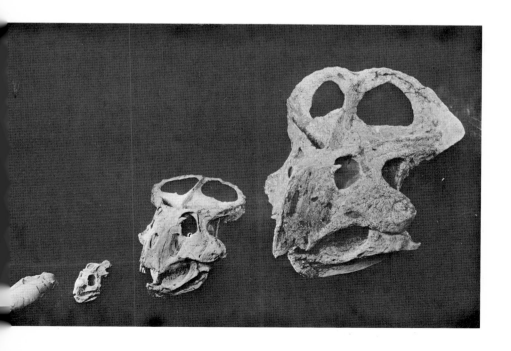

Protoceratops *skeletons and a nest of eggs.*

on, and brought fame overnight to the men from the museum. Olsen's eggs were no more important to science than Shackelford's skull, but they did bring the publicity that helped in raising funds to keep the expedition in the field.

Now the *Protoceratops* life series seemed as complete as anyone could wish, starting right from the egg. But more was to come. The embryos inside two of the shells had been preserved. There was no question left as to whether these eggs were really laid by dinosaurs. The embryos were so much like the baby *Protoceratops* that there could be no mistake. Paleo-detectives had believed that some of the dinosaurs probably laid eggs. But now they knew. Here was absolute proof.

Dinosaurs had been known for many years. Why had no one found their eggs before? The rocks of the Flaming Cliffs gave a clue. Wind-ripple markings showed that the rocks had once been sand dunes. Like a turtle, the mother *Protoceratops* had scooped out a hole, laid her eggs in it, carefully covered them with sand, and gone off to let the warmth of the sun do the hatching. If all went well, the sun shone and the eggs hatched. But where there are sand dunes, there are sandstorms. If a storm came up before hatching day, the nest could be buried so deep in sand that the baby dinosaurs wouldn't be able to break out of the eggs. Or, if hatching time was not yet near, the little animals developing in the eggs could simply have died for lack of air.

Dinosaurs of all ages may have been trapped in this area by the same kind of storms. At least, their skeletons were found in the same kind of rock as the eggs were. They may have settled down to wait out a heavy storm and learned, too late, that they could not wiggle out from under the drifted sand. This might account for the fine skeletons. The dinosaurs were buried so deep, and so quickly, that marauding animals who generally tear bodies apart and scatter bones did not find them.

Protoceratops was not very large, as dinosaurs go. The biggest skeleton found was about nine feet long. The smallest one was in an egg eight inches long. Some kinds of dinosaurs were over fifty feet long.

Protoceratops was a plant eater, but its teeth were not at all like the flat grinders in the cow's jaws. Its teeth were pointed and rather thin. They looked a little like arrowheads with long shafts. But they did make a good grinding surface, because there were a great many of them.

You remember that the cow's upper grinding teeth fit down on top of the lower ones, and grinding takes place as the lower jaw moves from side to side. The jaw hinge in *Protoceratops* shows that there was no slack for side-to-side motion. Besides, the upper teeth fit outside the lowers, so food must have been ground with an up-and-down chewing motion.

Both the upper and lower jaws had a double row of those pointed teeth on each side. There were about fifteen teeth in one row that were fully grown out into chewing position. In a row alongside of this first row were fifteen more

Side view of the lower jaw of Protoceratops, *showing the arrangement of teeth.*

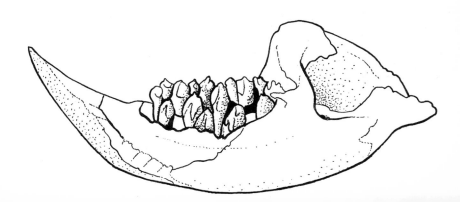

teeth. If a tooth from the first row should be lost, a replacement would grow in from the second row. This second row was apparently used in chewing along with the first row. So the complete set numbered about 120 teeth at one time. But there were still more sets of teeth out of sight in the jaw. No one knows exactly how many sets of teeth there were during the lifetime of a *Protoceratops*. However, there is some evidence that about 500 teeth might have been a lifetime supply.

In addition to the many grinding teeth, *Protoceratops* had two small teeth on each side of its upper jaw, up near the front. They probably weren't very useful, because they were right behind a very heavy, sturdy beak. Certainly, the beak should have been a very effective implement whether the little teeth were there or not. Perhaps, like the spare toe of *Merychippus,* they just hadn't yet disappeared.

The beak was much like the one in the modern-day turtle. It consisted of a hard, horny covering for the tip of the upper jaw, and a smaller one for the lower. It must have served very well as a defensive weapon. With heavy jaw and neck muscles, *Protoceratops* might have been able to snap the bones of its enemies in two with a single twist of that beak. Such a hook could have been used—and probably was—to pull up edible roots, or to break small tree branches for food.

A small hump behind the beak has been of interest to

Restoration of the head of Protoceratops.

scientists. It is not big enough to have served any known purpose. Around it, the grain of the bone shows a pattern like the one around the nose horn of some later dinosaurs. If *Protoceratops* is the ancestor of *Triceratops,* then this little nose hump can be considered the ancestor of the nose horn. Unlike the front teeth, which are on the way out, this hump appears to be a feature on the way in.

In *Protoceratops,* the head doesn't stop where the neck begins. Instead the bone at the back of the skull extends to the rear, forming a shield over the neck. This is known as the frill, and the two holes in it are "fenestrae"—Latin for "windows." The frill served as a muscle-attachment area and as a protector over the neck.

Both the top and bottom surfaces of the frill provided broad flat areas of bone where large muscles could be anchored. For still firmer attachment, a ridge extended up the middle of the top side, and on up over the crown of the skull. The jaw muscles were attached to the forward part, and the rest was covered by the neck muscles that moved the big head around. As long muscles contract, they bunch up like a strong man's biceps. Apparently the fenestrae were just holes where the muscles could bunch up. All of the evidence points to strong, heavy muscles for the jaws and the neck. This checks with the fact that the head was massive in relation to the rest of the skeleton. Only a good set of muscles could have made a useful thing of it.

Because the neck is a vital spot, many dinosaurs' lives must have been saved by the protective frill. In fact, the protection given by the frill was so good that the usual bony covering of the spinal cord was weak. Most animals have heavy neck vertebrae for that purpose. *Protoceratops* had only partial cover; its neck vertebrae did not make a complete circle around the spinal cord, but were open on the upper side. Some think this is a very important point. The spinal cord would be more flexible than one encased in a bony pipeline. They think the jarring of such a heavy head might have broken a more rigid cord. Certainly, jarring would take place in fighting and in the normal food-getting process of breaking branches.

Protoceratops must have been as graceful as a dog with a dachshund front and a greyhound rear. Its front legs were shorter than its hind legs. Its upper arms stuck straight out from its sides, supported by vertical forearms. But its hind legs were close to its body and more nearly straight from bottom to top. It was midway between the primitive and advanced limb arrangements sketched earlier—like this:

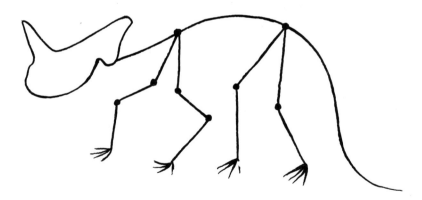

This fact is shown by the shapes of the various bones at the joints and the way they fit together. Animals that have the stick-out kind of front leg have long shoulder blades.

Protoceratops had long shoulder blades and the muscle-attachment bumps on the leg bones that go with that position. So far as the hind leg is concerned, there is more evidence. The upper leg bone was shorter than the lower leg bones. This is the case in animals that have the forward-backward swinging leg motion. It is not true of animals whose legs stick straight out from the hip.

A paleo-detective might wonder if this oddity of limbs meant that the animal walked on its hind feet. It hardly seems likely. In the first place, the large head must have been too heavy for good hind-footed balance. Second, the bones of the front legs were heavy enough to have supported the weight, even though they were not as massive as the bones in the hind limbs.

Protoceratops' toes were fairly long and must have had a good deal of spring in them. The tips of the digits had either strong nails or small hooves. The present-day foot most like these has one large pad on the bottom, located between the toes but back behind the tip joints. Probably *Protoceratops* had a similar pad. The front feet and hind feet were much alike except that the front ones were smaller.

Such feet would be best used on solid ground. That is, they were not broad enough for marshlands, and they certainly were not built for swimming, digging or flying. They were more like those of cats and dogs. *Protoceratops* could be expected to have lived in the same kind of country. Fossil trees from the rocks where the bones were found are much like trees that we know today. They are the kinds we would expect to find along streams in fairly dry, flat country. This evidence fits nicely with the feeding habits shown by the beak and teeth. Legs, feet, beak and teeth were about what an animal would need to live on woody plants. The widespread front legs would have braced the body while the big head was twisted from side to side in breaking branches. When necessary, *Protoceratops* could have hooked his beak over a limb or under a root and given a tremendous pull with the big hind legs.

Archaeopteryx lithographica gave strong evidence that birds are closely related to reptiles. In the same way, *Protoceratops* gave evidence that the lumbering *Triceratops* was descended from a little dinosaur that ran about on its hind legs. In almost every way the leg and foot structure of *Protoceratops* was between the earlier condition and the later *Triceratops*.

Some features of *Protoceratops'* anatomy seem to mean only that it was on the way from ancestors to descendants. For example, it had seven or eight vertebrae fused for attachment of the hipbones. That was a stronger arrangement than the small ancestral two-legged dinosaur had, but not as good as the ten fused vertebrae in *Triceratops*. Also, the vertebrae near the base of the tail had high spines for

Reconstruction of Protoceratops.

strong muscles. These are often found in swimming animals such as crocodiles. Some people believe, for that reason, that *Protoceratops* was a strong swimmer. There is so much evidence that it lived on dry land, it seems more likely that the tail spines were just another feature on the way out.

Several people have made reconstructions of *Protoceratops*. All of them look much alike. If a paleontologist were to make a new one, he might start with plaster casts of all the bones and build a complete skeleton in the position he chose. The head would be easy. He would build up the cheek muscles with plaster, as William Huff did with the bison. He would do the same under the frill where the great neck muscles were. He would put eyes in the eye sockets, and then construct a heavy, leatherlike skin. The original skin of *Protoceratops* was not actually preserved, but the sand on the underside of one skull formed a crust that had wrinkles in it, as skin might. Like the horn tips of the bison, this gave a strong clue. Besides, all known reptiles have some such covering. The paleontologist would leave the skin between the head and shoulder loose and baggy. It must have been loose, because the animal needed a lot of slack to turn its head with that big frill.

By reviewing all of the work that has been done on the muscles of dinosaurs and other reptiles, the scientist could build up the arm, leg, trunk and tail muscles one by one and be quite sure he was correct. This would be a long, tedious task, and he probably would not think it was necessary because he would know enough about the muscles that he could make the general shape of each part about right. Then he would imitate the skin, leaving folds and baggy places where it would have been stretched.

All in all, these paleo-detectives may know nearly as much about this 75-million-year-old animal as you know about your great-great-grandfather. They know the general shape of its body, what kind of food it ate, what kind of country it lived in. They can tell how it got around, and that its mate laid eggs. They know the major changes that took place in its body from the time it was an embryo in an egg until it was old. And with only a reasonable amount of guesswork, they know who its ancestors and its descendants were.

Some people are architects because they like to design houses. Some are nurses because they take pleasure in helping the sick. A few people are paleontologists. They find a deep satisfaction in adding to the world's knowledge about the history of life.

Perhaps one thing the paleontologist likes is that so much work is left to be done. The fossil record is far from complete, and the fossils already collected are not fully studied. Little is known of *Bison latifrons* except from a few skulls. There is a long, long blank between *Archaeopteryx lithographica* and its ancestors or its descendants. The same is true of *Protoceratops andrewsi,* and a multitude of other life forms.

Before the paleo-detective's job is well in hand and all the cases solved, there will be hundreds of George Olsens and J. B. Shackelfords gathering evidence from far places. There will be a great many Burnett Days happening onto important fossils right at home. And there will be a goodly number of Huffs and VanderHoofs working together so that the rest of us can see the full picture of life's history.

BIBLIOGRAPHY

BIBLIOGRAPHY

Andrews, Roy Chapman. *All About Dinosaurs.* Random House, 1953

Augusta, Joseph and Burian, Zdenek. *Prehistoric Animals.* London, Spring Books

Camp, Charles L. *Earth Song: A Prologue to History.* Berkeley, University of California Press, 1952

Colbert, Edwin H. *The Dinosaur Book.* Published for the American Museum of Natural History by McGraw-Hill Book Co., 2d ed., 1951

Knight, Charles R. *Before the Dawn of History.* Whittlesey House, 1935

Knight, Charles R. *Life through the Ages.* Knopf, 1946

Life, Editorial Staff of and Barnett, Lincoln. "The World We Live In." Time, Inc., 1955

Scheele, William Earl. *First Mammals.* World Publishing Co., 1955

Scheele, William Earl. *Prehistoric Animals.* World Publishing Co., 1954

White, Anne Terry. *Prehistoric America.* Random House, 1951

INDEX

INDEX

115